Guest Spot

CW00409674

CLASSICS
Playalong *for* Violin

WISE PUBLICATIONS
London/New York/Paris/Sydney/Copenhagen/Madrid

Music Sales Limited
8/9 Frith Street, London W1V 5TZ, England.
Music Sales Corporation
257 Park Avenue South, New York, NY10010, USA.
Music Sales Pty Limited
120 Rothschild Avenue, Rosebery, NSW 2018, Australia.

Order No. AM955560
ISBN 0-7119-7361-X
This book © Copyright 1999 by Wise Publications.

Unauthorised reproduction of any part of this publication by
any means including photocopying is an infringement of copyright.

Book design by Michael Bell Design.
Music arranged by Paul Honey.
Music processed by Enigma Music Production Services.
Cover photography by George Taylor.
Printed in the United Kingdom by Page Bros., Norwich, Norfolk.

CD produced by Paul Honey.
Instrumental solos by Mark Denman.
Engineered by Kester Sims.

Your Guarantee of Quality:
As publishers, we strive to produce every book to
the highest commercial standards.
The music has been freshly engraved and the book has been
carefully designed to minimise awkward page turns and
to make playing from it a real pleasure.
Particular care has been given to specifying acid-free, neutralized
paper made from pulps which have not been elemental chlorine bleached.
This pulp is from farmed sustainable forests and was
produced with special regard for the environment.
Throughout, the printing and binding have been planned to
ensure a sturdy, attractive publication which should give years of enjoyment.
If your copy fails to meet our high standards,
please inform us and we will gladly replace it.

Music Sales' complete catalogue describes thousands of
titles and is available in full colour sections by subject,
direct from Music Sales Limited.
Please state your areas of interest and send a
cheque/postal order for £1.50 for postage to:
Music Sales Limited, Newmarket Road, Bury St. Edmunds, Suffolk IP33 3YB.

Ave Maria

Based on Bach's Prelude No.1 in C Major

Composed by Charles Gounod

Andante

© Copyright 1999 Dorsey Brothers Music Limited, 8/9 Frith Street, London W1.
All Rights Reserved. International Copyright Secured.

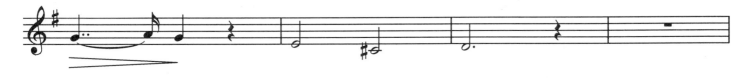

Air On The 'G' String

Composed by Johann Sebastian Bach

Larghetto

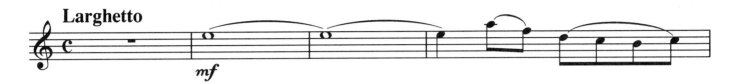

© Copyright 1999 Dorsey Brothers Music Limited, 8/9 Frith Street, London W1.
All Rights Reserved. International Copyright Secured.

Habañera

from Carmen

Composed by Georges Bizet

Andantino

© Copyright 1999 Dorsey Brothers Music Limited, 8/9 Frith Street, London W1.
All Rights Reserved. International Copyright Secured.

Jupiter
from The Planets Suite

Composed by Gustav Holst

Andante maestoso

© Copyright 1923 J. Curwen & Sons Limited, 8/9 Frith Street, London W1V 5TZ.
All Rights Reserved. International Copyright Secured.

New World Symphony

Theme

Composed by Antonin Dvořák

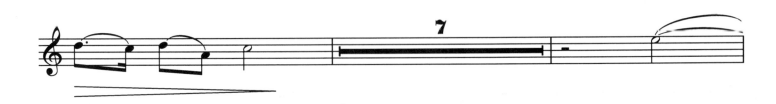

© Copyright 1999 Dorsey Brothers Music Limited, 8/9 Frith Street, London W1.
All Rights Reserved. International Copyright Secured.

Ode To Joy

Theme from Symphony No.9 'Choral'

Composed by Ludwig van Beethoven

Allegro

© Copyright 1999 Dorsey Brothers Music Limited, 8/9 Frith Street, London W1.
All Rights Reserved. International Copyright Secured.

Rondo in D Minor

from Abdelazer

Composed by Henry Purcell
As used in Young Person's Guide To The Orchestra - Britten

© Copyright 1999 Dorsey Brothers Music Limited, 8/9 Frith Street, London W1.
All Rights Reserved. International Copyright Secured.

Spring

from The Four Seasons

Composed by Antonio Vivaldi

Allegro

© Copyright 1999 Dorsey Brothers Music Limited, 8/9 Frith Street, London W1.
All Rights Reserved. International Copyright Secured.

Hornpipe
from The Water Music

Composed by George Frideric Handel

Allegro

© Copyright 1999 Dorsey Brothers Music Limited, 8/9 Frith Street, London W1.
All Rights Reserved. International Copyright Secured.

Swan Lake

Theme

Composed by Peter Ilyich Tchaikovsky

Moderato

© Copyright 1999 Dorsey Brothers Music Limited, 8/9 Frith Street, London W1.
All Rights Reserved. International Copyright Secured.

rall.   più mosso

11/99 (35808)